Rhyme time

Rhyming words are words which end with the same sound.

■ Copy the rhymes from the coins into the correct piggy bank.

■ Use look, say, cover, write, check to practise all the words.

Tick here when you have checked your work.

Wriggling W

The words in this puzzle all have a **W** in the spelling which we do not say. The **W** is silent.

■ Fit the words from the box into the maze.
    Some letters are given to help you.

answer	wren	wriggle	wrist
sword	wrench	wring	write
wreck	wrestle	wrinkle	writing

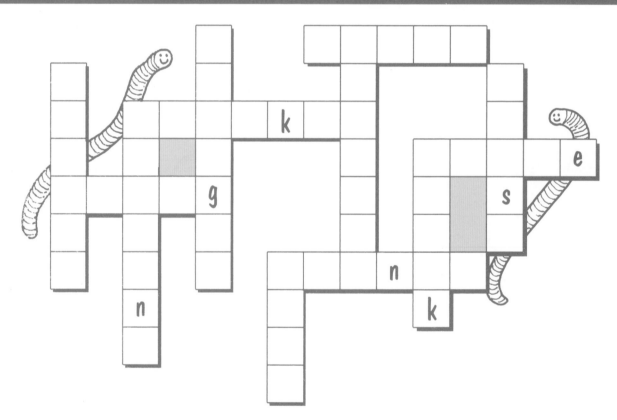

■ Use look, (say,) cover, write, check to practise all the words.

_____   _____   _____

_____   _____   _____

_____   _____   _____

_____

Tick here when you have checked your work. ☐

Knowing **kn**

Some words begin with the letter **k**, even though they sound as if they begin with **n**, e.g. <u>kn</u>eel and <u>kn</u>ack.

■ Can you unscramble all these silent **k** words and fit them into the puzzle?

If you get them right, you will find another silent **k** word written down the middle.

1. tonk
2. nniittkg
3. conkk
4. ownk
5. kenluck
6. feink
7. daken
8. thingk
9. eken

■ The hidden word is _____.

■ Use l**oo**k, (say,) cover, write, ch**e**ck to practise all the words.

_____ _____ _____

_____ _____ _____

_____

Tick here when you have checked your work. ☐

Emphasising ciphers

Oh no! The computer has used a cipher (a code) to print out these words.

■ Use this cipher to find the words.

a	b	c	d	e	f	g	h	i	j	k	l	m	n	o	p	q	r	s	t	u	v	w	x	y	z
26	25	24	23	22	21	20	19	18	17	16	15	14	13	12	11	10	9	8	7	6	5	4	3	2	1

(i) 20 9 26 11 19 ⇨ (i) _ _ _ _ _

(ii) 22 15 22 11 19 26 13 7 ⇨ (ii) _ _ _ _ _ _ _ _

(iii) 11 19 9 26 8 22 ⇨ (iii) _ _ _ _ _ _

(iv) 8 11 19 22 9 22 ⇨ (iv) _ _ _ _ _ _

(v) 11 19 26 13 7 12 14 ⇨ (v) _ _ _ _ _ _ _

(vi) 22 14 11 19 26 8 18 8 ⇨ (vi) _ _ _ _ _ _ _ _

(vii) 11 19 12 13 22 ⇨ (vii) _ _ _ _ _

(viii) 11 19 2 8 18 24 26 15 ⇨ (viii) _ _ _ _ _ _ _ _

(ix) 8 18 11 19 12 13 ⇨ (ix) _ _ _ _ _ _

(x) 11 19 12 7 12 ⇨ (x) _ _ _ _ _

(xi) 20 12 11 19 22 9 ⇨ (xi) _ _ _ _ _ _

(xii) 8 26 11 11 19 18 9 22 ⇨ (xii) _ _ _ _ _ _ _ _

■ Use look, (say,) cover, write, check to practise all the words.

_____   _____   _____

_____   _____   _____

_____   _____   _____

_____   _____   _____

Tick here when you have checked your work. ☐

The answers to this crossword all have something in common.

■ Solve the puzzle and then explain what the answers have in common.

ACROSS

3. Making, constructing
6. A fellow
7. People who keep something safe
8. Used to taste things
9. A visitor in your home

DOWN

1. Americans call this a cookie
2. Estimate
3. Purchase
4. A spy might wear this

5. A promise that something will work
6. A bad feeling when you have done something wrong

■ All these words have a silent _____.

■ Use look, say, cover, write, check to practise all the answers.

_____ _____ _____

_____ _____ _____

_____ _____ _____

_____

Tick here when you have checked your work. ☐

Crazy catacomb!

The words in this puzzle all have something in common.
What pattern do they share?

■ Fit the words into the maze. Some letters are given to help you.

bomb
climb
crumb
honeycomb

lamb
limbs
numb
plumber
succumb
thumb
tomb
womb

■ All these words have a silent _____.

■ Use l👁👁k, (say,) cover, write, check ✓ to practise all the words.

_____ _____ _____

_____ _____ _____

_____ _____ _____

Tick here when you have checked your work. ☐

Quantities of qua

■ Use this code to discover more words which contain the letters **qua**.

1	2	3	4	5	6	7	8	9	10	11	12	13	14	15	16	17	18	19	20	21	22	23	24	25	26
a	b	c	d	e	f	g	h	i	j	k	l	m	n	o	p	q	r	s	t	u	v	w	x	y	z

(i) | 17 | 21 | 1 | 18 | 20 | 5 | 18 | = _ _ _ _ _ _ _

(ii) | 17 | 21 | 1 | 18 | 1 | 14 | 20 | 9 | 14 | 5 | = _ _ _ _ _ _ _ _ _ _

(iii) | 17 | 21 | 1 | 12 | 9 | 6 | 25 | = _ _ _ _ _ _ _

(iv) | 17 | 21 | 1 | 12 | 9 | 20 | 25 | = _ _ _ _ _ _ _

(v) | 17 | 21 | 1 | 14 | 20 | 9 | 20 | 25 | = _ _ _ _ _ _ _ _

(vi) | 17 | 21 | 1 | 18 | 18 | 5 | 12 | = _ _ _ _ _ _ _

(vii) | 17 | 21 | 1 | 18 | 18 | 25 | = _ _ _ _ _ _

(viii) | 17 | 21 | 1 | 18 | 20 | 26 | = _ _ _ _ _ _

(ix) | 19 | 17 | 21 | 1 | 2 | 2 | 12 | 5 | = _ _ _ _ _ _ _ _

(x) | 19 | 17 | 21 | 1 | 20 | = _ _ _ _ _

(xi) | 19 | 17 | 21 | 1 | 19 | 8 | = _ _ _ _ _ _

(xii) | 19 | 17 | 21 | 1 | 14 | 4 | 5 | 18 | = _ _ _ _ _ _ _ _

■ What sound does the letter **a** make
when it follows **qu** in these words?_____

■ Use l**oo**k, (say,) cover, write, ch**e**ck to practise all the words.

_____   _____   _____

_____   _____   _____

_____   _____   _____

_____   _____   _____

Tick here when you have checked your work. ☐

Wacky words

English is full of words which can be tricky to spell!

■ Fit the tricky words from the box into the trains.

blood	country	none	separate
business	exercise	muscle	sugar
certain	impatient	necessary	sure
column	jewellery	restaurant	some

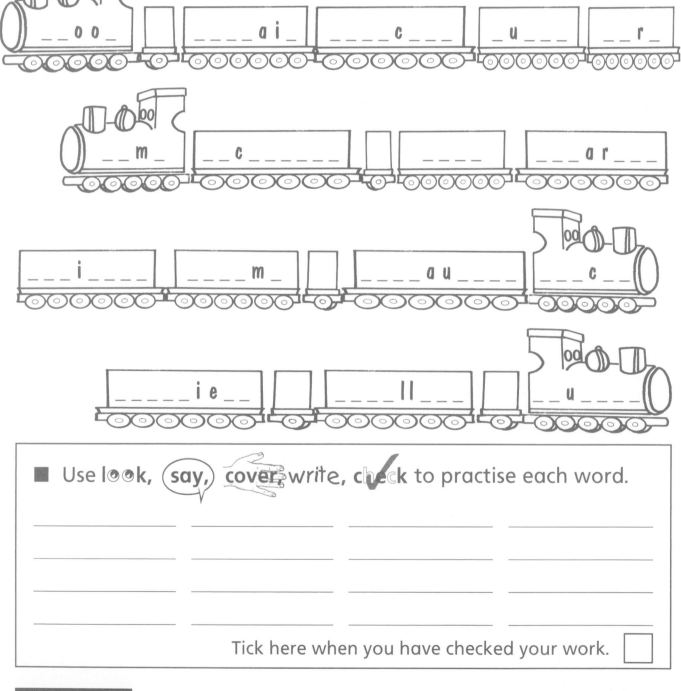

■ Use look, (say,) cover, write, check to practise each word.

_____   _____   _____

_____   _____   _____

_____   _____   _____

_____   _____   _____

Tick here when you have checked your work. ☐

Page 10

Compound crackers

In English we often join two words together to make a new one,
e.g. **motor + way = motorway.**

■ Join the two halves of each cracker back together to make
   one word.

over   one   paper   sill

neck   stretched   window   back

cup   day   sun   brush

every   lace   tow   shine

half   way   tooth   bar

birth   board   sea   side

■ Use **look, say, cover, write, check** to practise each new word.

_____   _____   _____

_____   _____   _____

_____   _____   _____

Tick here when you have checked your work. ☐

Searching for **ea**

ea as **ĕ**

In some words the letters **ea** say **e**, e.g. in **br<u>ea</u>d**, or **w<u>ea</u>ther**.

■ The letters **ea** have been missed out of these words.
Put the letters **ea** back into each word and write out the whole word.

1 rdy _____

2 stdy _____

3 msure _____

4 lther _____

5 hlthy _____

6 drdful _____

7 trsure _____

8 plsure _____

9 wlth _____

10 hd _____

11 stlthily _____

12 mdow _____

■ Now circle each of the completed words in this word ribbon.
The first one has been done for you.

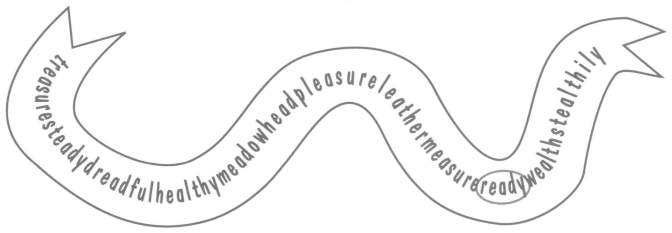

treasuresteadydreadfulhealthymeadowheadpleasureleathermeasure(ready)wealthstealthily

■ Use l**oo**k, (**say,**) **cover,** write, check to practise all the words.

_____ _____ _____

_____ _____ _____

_____ _____ _____

Tick here when you have checked your work. ☐

Awful aw

In these words the letters **aw** sound like **o**.

■ Draw a circle round the letters **aw** in each word.

■ Find and circle each word in the wordsearch.
  The words may be written in any direction, forwards or backwards.
  The first one is done for you.

awful ✓   paw
awkward   pawn
bawl   prawn
brawl   raw
brawn   saw
claw   shawl
crawl   sprawl
draw   strawberry
drawl   tawny
flawed   trawler
gnaw   yawn
law

c	r	a	w	l	l	w	a	h	s
w	l	w	a	r	b	i	n	a	t
f	l	a	w	e	d	b	w	t	r
t	r	a	w	l	e	r	a	h	a
d	n	w	a	p	r	a	r	p	w
g	d	r	a	w	l	w	p	a	b
l	w	a	r	p	s	n	r	w	e
a	l	w	a	b	w	d	w	a	r
n	a	d	r	a	w	k	w	a	r
a	w	f	u	l	t	a	w	n	y

■ Use look, (say,) cover, write, check to practise the words
  which are underlined.

_____   _____   _____

_____   _____   _____

_____   _____   _____

Tick here when you have checked your work. ☐

Lovely O

In some words the letter **o** sounds like **u**, e.g. s<u>o</u>n, gl<u>o</u>ve, m<u>o</u>ther.
All the words in this puzzle have an **o** which makes a **u** sound.

■ Unscramble these words and then fit them into the puzzle to
   reveal the mystery word.

1. emoc _____
2. yomen _____
3. hontm _____
4. tronf _____
5. node _____
6. hotre _____
7. herbrot _____
8. Maynod _____
9. beavo _____
10. vole _____
11. heovs _____

■ The mystery word is _____.

■ Use l**oo**k, (**say,**) cover, write, ch**eck** to practise each word.

_____ _____ _____

_____ _____ _____

_____ _____ _____

Tick here when you have checked your work. ☐

Scouting for **ou**

When the vowels **o** and **u** come next to each other they can make an **ow** sound, e.g. sc<u>ou</u>t, <u>ou</u>r, <u>ou</u>t.

■ The letters **ou** have been missed out of these words. Put these vowels back into each word, and write out the whole word.

1 mntain _____

2 cnt _____

3 hr _____

4 thsands _____

5 dbt _____

6 accnt _____

7 prd _____

8 annnce _____

9 surrnd _____

10 amnt _____

11 cncil _____

12 sth _____

■ Now circle each of the completed words in this word ribbon. The first one is done for you.

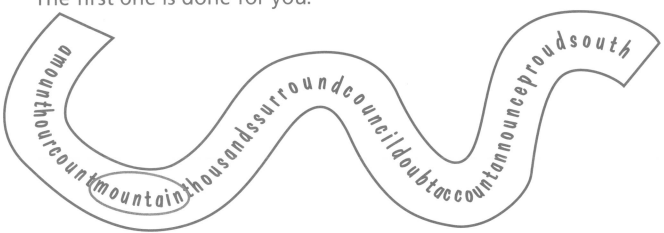

■ Use lo**o**k, say, cover, write, check to practise each word.

_____ _____ _____

_____ _____ _____

_____ _____ _____

_____ _____ _____

Tick here when you have checked your work. ☐

y as a vowel

The letter **y** is a consonant but in some words it acts as a vowel, e.g. *shy, dry, sycamore*.

■ Use this code and discover more mysterious **y** words.

15	16	17	18	19	20	21	22	23	24	25	26	1	2	3	4	5	6	7	8	9	10	11	12	13	14
a	b	c	d	e	f	g	h	i	j	k	l	m	n	o	p	q	r	s	t	u	v	w	x	y	z

(i)

22	13	1	2

= _ _ _ _

(ii)

17	13	1	16	15	26

= _ _ _ _ _ _

(iii)

7	13	1	16	3	26

= _ _ _ _ _ _

(iv)

6	22	13	8	22	1

= _ _ _ _ _ _

(v)

6	22	13	1	19

= _ _ _ _ _

(vi)

17	13	17	26	19

= _ _ _ _ _

(vii)

7	8	13	26	19

= _ _ _ _ _

(viii)

1	9	26	8	23	4	26	13

= _ _ _ _ _ _ _ _

(ix)

17	6	13	23	2	21

= _ _ _ _ _ _

(x)

4	13	8	22	3	2

= _ _ _ _ _ _

■ Use look, (say,) cover, write, check to practise each word.

_____   _____

_____   _____

_____

Tick here when you have checked your work. ☐

New Spellaway 2

Key Stage 2

Answers

About New Spellaway

New Spellaway is a series of four books which progressively cover Key Stage 2 in Spelling. The puzzles are designed to provide short, fun, educational sessions and to complement the formal teaching of spelling. Positive adult support such as offering help, further explanation or providing a dictionary is invaluable to the student. The series also offers children the opportunity to consolidate each new pattern or concept through the multi-sensory look, say, cover, write, check approach. Children can be further encouraged to keep their own alphabetical list of words they have learned for their future reference.

You may wish to separate this answer section from the questions. Carefully pull out the middle 8 pages, then push the wire stitching back into place.

Rhyme time

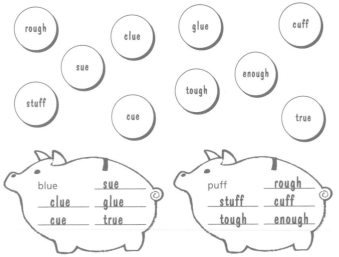

rough | clue | glue | cuff

sue

stuff | enough | tough | cue | true

blue — sue
clue — glue
cue — true

puff — rough
stuff — cuff
tough — enough

Wriggling w

answer	wren	wriggle	wrist
sword	wrench	wring	write
wreck	wrestle	wrinkle	writing

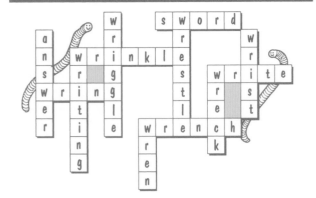

Knowing kn

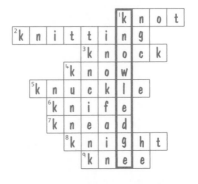

■ The hidden word is __knowledge__.

Emphasising ciphers

a	b	c	d	e	f	g	h	i	j	k	l	m	n	o	p	q	r	s	t	u	v	w	x	y	z
26	25	24	23	22	21	20	19	18	17	16	15	14	13	12	11	10	9	8	7	6	5	4	3	2	1

(i) 20 9 26 11 19 ⇨ (i) g r a p h
(ii) 22 15 22 11 19 26 13 7 ⇨ (ii) e l e p h a n t
(iii) 11 19 9 26 8 22 ⇨ (iii) p h r a s e
(iv) 8 11 19 22 9 22 ⇨ (iv) s p h e r e
(v) 11 19 26 13 7 12 14 ⇨ (v) p h a n t o m
(vi) 22 14 11 19 26 8 18 8 ⇨ (vi) e m p h a s i s
(vii) 11 19 12 13 22 ⇨ (vii) p h o n e
(viii) 11 19 2 8 18 24 26 15 ⇨ (viii) p h y s i c a l
(ix) 8 18 11 19 12 13 ⇨ (ix) s i p h o n
(x) 11 19 12 7 12 ⇨ (x) p h o t o
(xi) 20 12 11 19 22 9 ⇨ (xi) g o p h e r
(xii) 8 26 11 11 19 18 9 22 ⇨ (xii) s a p p h i r e

Building with u

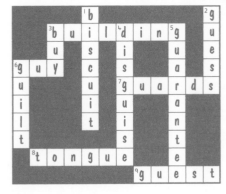

■ All these words have a silent ___u___.

Crazy catacomb!

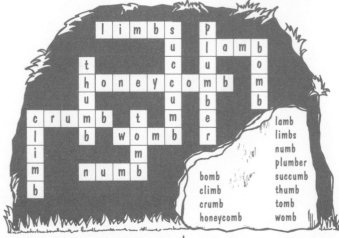

lamb
limbs
numb
plumber
bomb   succumb
climb   thumb
crumb   tomb
honeycomb womb

■ All these words have a silent ___b___.

Quantities of **qua**

1	2	3	4	5	6	7	8	9	10	11	12	13	14	15	16	17	18	19	20	21	22	23	24	25	26
a	b	c	d	e	f	g	h	i	j	k	l	m	n	o	p	q	r	s	t	u	v	w	x	y	z

(i)   17 21 1 18 20 5 18   = q u a r t e r
(ii)   17 21 1 18 1 14 20 9 14 5   = q u a r a n t i n e
(iii)   17 21 1 12 9 6 25   = q u a l i f y
(iv)   17 21 1 12 9 20 25   = q u a l i t y
(v)   17 21 1 14 20 9 20 25   = q u a n t i t y
(vi)   17 21 1 18 18 5 12   = q u a r r e l
(vii)   17 21 1 18 18 25   = q u a r r y
(viii)   17 21 1 18 20 26   = q u a r t z
(ix)   19 17 21 1 2 2 12 5   = s q u a b b l e
(x)   19 17 21 1 20   = s q u a t
(xi)   19 17 21 1 19 8   = s q u a s h
(xii)   19 17 21 1 14 4 5 18   = s q u a n d e r

■ What sound does the letter **a** make when it follows **qu** in these words?   **o**

Wacky words

blood   certain   exercise   sugar   sure

some   necessary   none   separate

business   column   restaurant   muscle

impatient   jewellery   country

Compound crackers

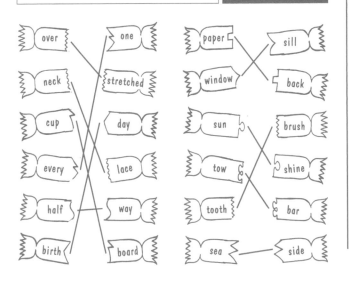

over — stretched
neck — lace
cup — day
every — one
half — way
birth — stretched

paper — back
window — sill
sun — shine
tow — brush
tooth — brush
sea — side
bar

Searching for **ea**

1. rdy   **ready**
2. stdy   **steady**
3. msure   **measure**
4. lther   **leather**
5. hlthy   **healthy**
6. drdful   **dreadful**
7. trsure   **treasure**
8. plsure   **pleasure**
9. with   **wealth**
10. hd   **head**
11. stlthily   **stealthily**
12. mdow   **meadow**

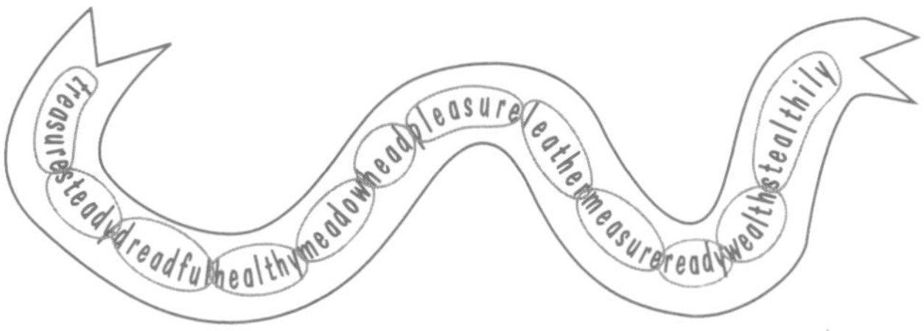

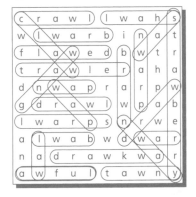

Awful **aw**

```
c r a w l   l w a h s
w l w a r b i n a t
f l a w e d b w t r
t r a w l e r a h a
d n w a p r a r p w
g d r a w w p a b
l w a r p s n r w e
a l w a b w d w a r
n a d r a w k w a r
a w f u l t a w n y
```

Some words may be found in more than one place in the grid, e.g. paw, raw.

Lovely **o**

1. emoc   **come**
2. yomen   **money**
3. hontm   **month**
4. tronf   **front**
5. node   **done**
6. hotre   **other**
7. herbrot   **brother**
8. Maynod   **Monday**
9. beavo   **above**
10. vole   **love**
11. heovs   **shove**

(Crossword grid:)
¹c o m e
²m o n e y
³m o n t h
⁴f r o n t
⁵d o n e
⁶o t h e r
⁷b r o t h e r
⁸M o n d a y
⁹a b o v e
¹⁰l o v e
¹¹s h o v e

■ The mystery word is   **comfortable** .

Scouting for **ou** — Page 15

1. mntain — **mountain**
2. cnt — **count**
3. hr — **hour**
4. thsands — **thousands**
5. dbt — **doubt**
6. accnt — **account**
7. prd — **proud**
8. annnce — **announce**
9. surrnd — **surround**
10. amnt — **amount**
11. cncil — **council**
12. sth — **south**

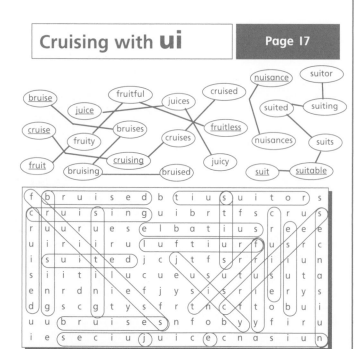

Mysterious **y** — Page 16

15	16	17	18	19	20	21	22	23	24	25	26	1	2	3	4	5	6	7	8	9	10	11	12	13	14
a	b	c	d	e	f	g	h	i	j	k	l	m	n	o	p	q	r	s	t	u	v	w	x	y	z

(i) 22 13 1 2 = **hymn**
(ii) 17 13 1 16 15 26 = **cymbal**
(iii) 7 13 1 16 3 26 = **symbol**
(iv) 6 22 13 8 22 1 = **rhythm**
(v) 6 22 13 1 19 = **rhyme**
(vi) 17 13 17 26 19 = **cycle**
(vii) 7 8 13 26 19 = **style**
(viii) 1 9 26 8 23 4 26 13 = **multiply**
(ix) 17 6 13 23 2 21 = **crying**
(x) 4 13 8 22 3 2 = **python**

Cruising with **ui** — Page 17

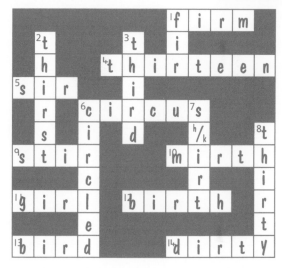

More compound crackers — Page 18

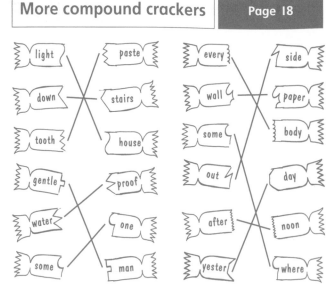

Flirting with **ir** — Page 19

1. firm
2. thirst
3. tired
4. thirteen
5. sir
6. circus
7. s
8. t
9. stir
10. mirth
11. girl
12. birth
13. bird
14. dirty

■ In these words the letters **ir** make the sound ___ur___.

Almost **al** — Page 20

1. most — **almost**
2. wl — **wall**
3. chk — **chalk**
4. appling — **appalling**
5. ready — **already**
6. st — **salt**
7. tking — **talking**
8. recl — **recall**
9. right — **alright**
10. tler — **taller**
11. bl — **ball**
12. flen — **fallen**

Answer page 4

Working with words — Page 21

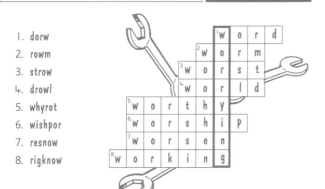

1. dorw
2. rowm
3. strow
4. drowl
5. whyrot
6. wishpor
7. resnow
8. rigknow

Crossword grid letters:
1. w o r d
2. w o r m
3. w o r s t
4. w o r l d
5. w o r t h y
6. w o r s h i p
7. w o r s e n
8. w o r k i n g

■ The mystery word is __worrying__.

Matching tch — Page 22

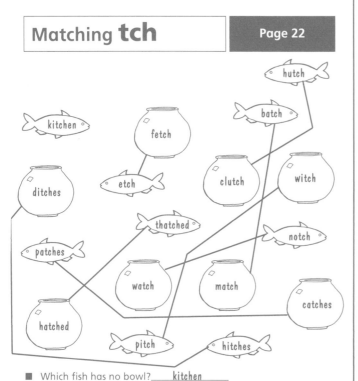

hutch, batch, kitchen, fetch, etch, clutch, witch, ditches, thatched, notch, patches, watch, match, catches, hatched, pitch, hitches

■ Which fish has no bowl? __kitchen__

An ey journey — Page 23

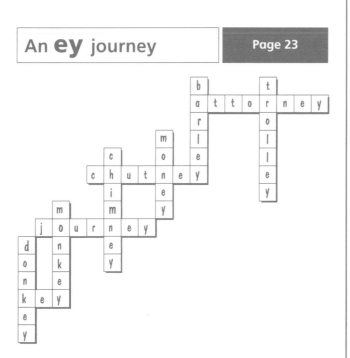

attorney, chutney, money, trolley, journey, chimney, monkey, donkey

Sheaves of ves — Page 24

Crossword:
3. l e a v e s
4. s (haves / shaves)
1. h
2. s
5. c a l v e s
6. h
7. w o l v e s
8. e l v e s
9. s h e l v e s

■ Rule: To make these into plurals, change _f_ to _ve_ and add _s_.

Stories of ies — Page 25

1. baby ⇒ __babies__
2. cry ⇒ __cries__
3. curry ⇒ __curries__
4. entry ⇒ __entries__
5. forgery ⇒ __forgeries__
6. lady ⇒ __ladies__
7. lorry ⇒ __lorries__
8. mystery ⇒ __mysteries__
9. sky ⇒ __skies__
10. spy ⇒ __spies__
11. supply ⇒ __supplies__
12. worry ⇒ __worries__

Word search grid:
skies, spies, mystery, babies, curries

Pay attention to tion — Page 26

1. in vi ta con tion
2. re sta tion
3. con sid di tion
4. sub frac tion
5. de a tten a tion
6. mul ti pli ca tion
7. sub road trac tion
8. add ac tion tion
9. re co rrec ord tion
10. punc tu sat a tion
11. in terr down up tion
12. fic sit or stand tion

Answer page 5

Presenting **ent**

Page 27

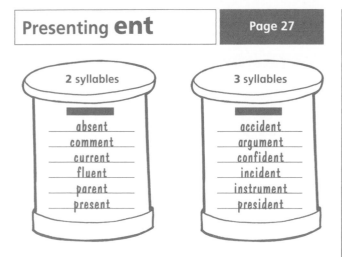

2 syllables
absent
comment
current
fluent
parent
present

3 syllables
accident
argument
confident
incident
instrument
president

Varying verbs

Page 30

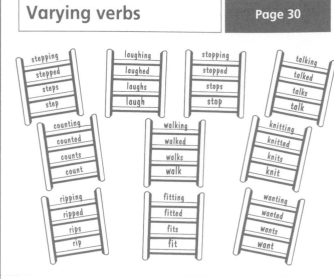

stepping / stepped / steps / step

laughing / laughed / laughs / laugh

stopping / stopped / stops / stop

talking / talked / talks / talk

counting / counted / counts / count

walking / walked / walks / walk

knitting / knitted / knits / knit

ripping / ripped / rips / rip

fitting / fitted / fits / fit

wanting / wanted / wants / want

Altering adjectives

Page 28

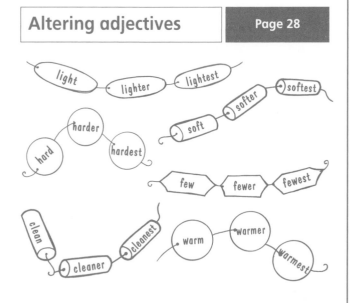

light — lighter — lightest

soft — softer — softest

hard — harder — hardest

few — fewer — fewest

clean — cleaner — cleanest

warm — warmer — warmest

Megapuzzle

Page 31

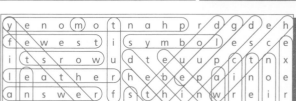

■ Arrange the ten unused letters to find the mystery word.

<u>r</u> <u>e</u> <u>s</u> <u>t</u> <u>a</u> <u>u</u> <u>r</u> <u>a</u> <u>n</u> <u>t</u>

Altering adjectives 2

Page 29

1.	hot	hotter	hottest
2.	flat	flatter	flattest
3.	high	higher	highest
4.	fast	faster	fastest
5.	wet	wetter	wettest
6.	fat	fatter	fattest
7.	sharp	sharper	sharpest
8.	cold	colder	coldest
9.	dark	darker	darkest
10.	sad	sadder	saddest
11.	short	shorter	shortest
12.	bright	brighter	brightest

New Spellaway 2

Key Stage 2

Answers

Cruising with **ui**

In these words the vowels **ui** make an **oo** sound.
Unfortunately these **ui** families have got jumbled up!

■ Link the families together (the first one is done for you).
Then find <u>all</u> the words in the wordsearch.

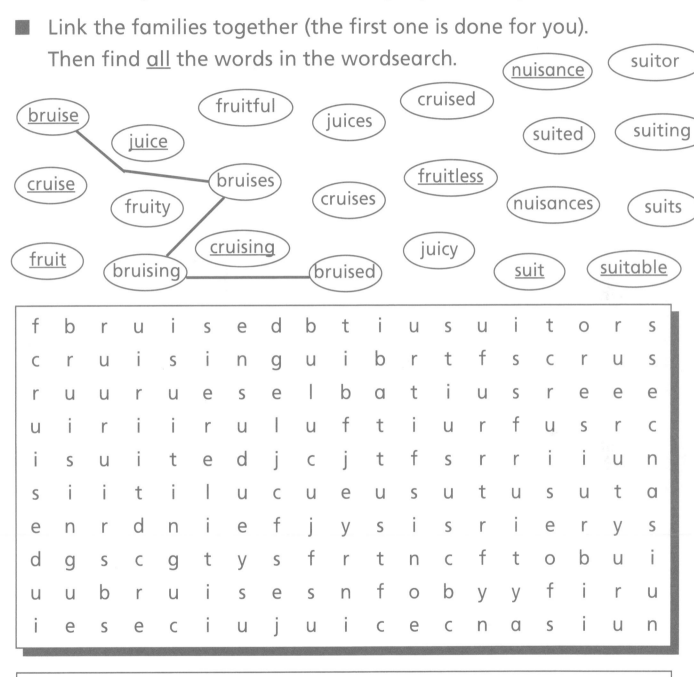

f	b	r	u	i	s	e	d	b	t	i	u	s	u	i	t	o	r	s
c	r	u	i	s	i	n	g	u	i	b	r	t	f	s	c	r	u	s
r	u	u	r	u	e	s	e	l	b	a	t	i	u	s	r	e	e	e
u	i	r	i	i	r	u	l	u	f	t	i	u	r	f	u	s	r	c
i	s	u	i	t	e	d	j	c	j	t	f	s	r	r	i	i	u	n
s	i	i	t	i	l	u	c	u	e	u	s	u	t	u	s	u	t	a
e	n	r	d	n	i	e	f	j	y	s	i	s	r	i	e	r	y	s
d	g	s	c	g	t	y	s	f	r	t	n	c	f	t	o	b	u	i
u	u	b	r	u	i	s	e	s	n	f	o	b	y	y	f	i	r	u
i	e	s	e	c	i	u	j	u	i	c	e	c	n	a	s	i	u	n

■ Use look, say, cover, write, check to practise the <u>underlined</u> words.

_____   _____   _____

_____   _____   _____

_____   _____   _____

Tick here when you have checked your work. ☐

More compound crackers

In English we often join two words together to make a new one, e.g. cow + boy = cowboy.

■ Join the two halves of each cracker back together to make one word.

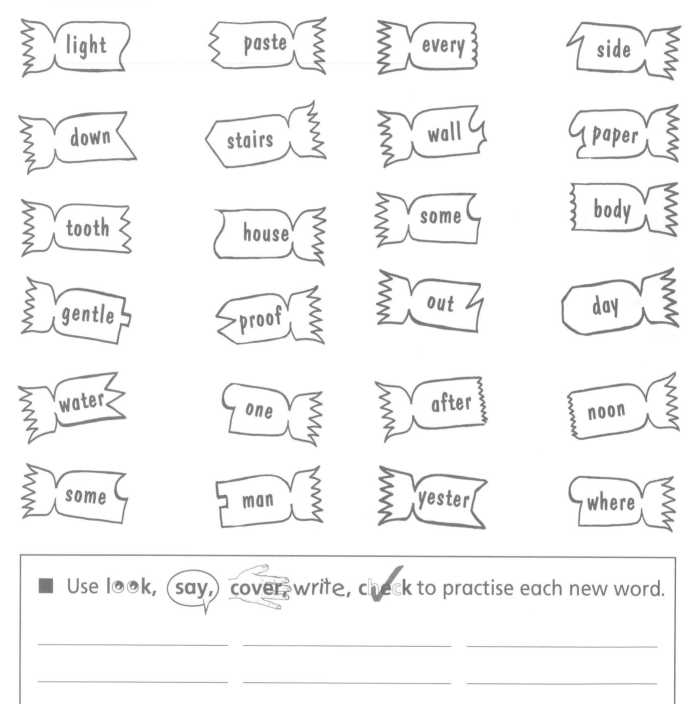

■ Use l⊙⊙k, say, cover, write, check to practise each new word.

_____   _____   _____

_____   _____   _____

_____   _____   _____

_____   _____   _____

Tick here when you have checked your work. ☐

Page 18

Flirting with ir

The answers to this crossword each contain the letters **ir**.

■ Find the answers then complete the rule for these words.

ACROSS

1. Secure, steady
4. Seven add six
5. A polite way of addressing a man
6. You might see clowns and jugglers here
9. You can use a spoon to do this
10. Laughter, enjoyment
11. Opposite of boy
12. When someone is born
13. Creature with feathers
14. Not clean

DOWN

1. Kind of tree with cones
2. The need to have a drink
3. First, second, _____.
6. Drew a ring round
7. Type of clothing
8. Fifteen add fifteen

■ In these words the letters **ir** make the sound _____.

■ Use look, (say,) cover, write, check to practise all the words.

_____ _____ _____ _____

_____ _____ _____ _____

_____ _____ _____ _____

_____ _____ _____ _____

Tick here when you have checked your work. ☐

Almost **al**

The letter **a** can sometimes make an **o** sound when it is followed by the letter **l**, for example in <u>al</u>so, <u>al</u>most and <u>al</u>l.

■ The letters **al** have been missed out of these words.
Replace these letters and write out the completed word.

1 most _____
2 wl _____
3 chk _____
4 appling _____
5 ready _____
6 st _____
7 tking _____
8 recl _____
9 right _____
10 tler _____
11 bl _____
12 flen _____

■ Find and circle each completed word.
The first one is done for you.

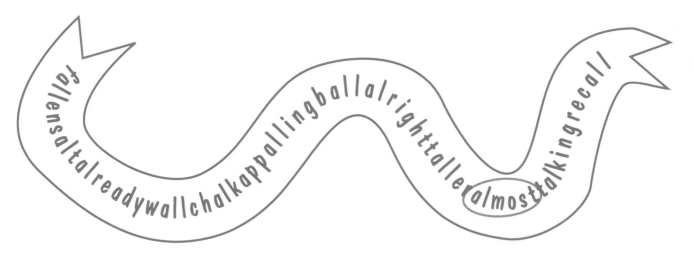

fallensaltalreadywallchalkappallingballalrighttalleralmosttalkingrecall

■ Use look, (say,) cover, write, check to practise each word.

_____ _____ _____ _____

_____ _____ _____ _____

_____ _____ _____ _____

Tick here when you have checked your work. ☐

Working with words

or as ŭr

In some words the letters **wor** sound like **wur**,
e.g. <u>wor</u>se, <u>wor</u>th and <u>wor</u>k.

■ Unscramble these **wor** words and fit them into the puzzle to reveal the mystery word.

1. dorw
2. rowm
3. strow
4. drowl
5. whyrot
6. wishpor
7. resnow
8. rigknow

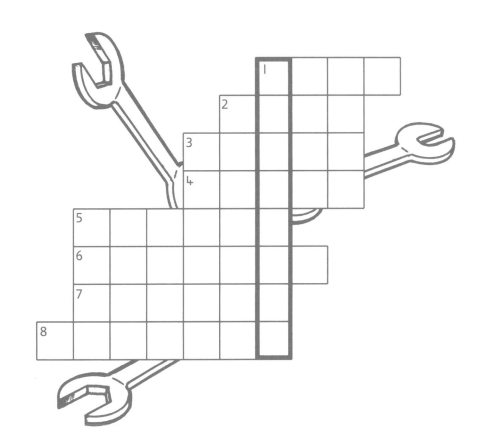

■ The mystery word is _____.

■ Use l⊙⊙k, (say,) cover, write, check to practise each word.

_____   _____   _____

_____   _____   _____

_____   _____

Tick here when you have checked your work. ☐

All these words contain the letter pattern **tch**.

■ Match each fish to the bowl which rhymes.
  One fish has no matching bowl.

hutch

kitchen

fetch

batch

ditches

etch

clutch

witch

thatched

notch

patches

watch

match

catches

hatched

pitch

hitches

■ Which fish has no bowl?_____

■ Use look, (say,) cover, write, check to practise the words
  in the bowls.

_____ _____ _____

_____ _____ _____

Tick here when you have checked your work. ☐

An **ey** journey

The letters **ey** make an **ee** sound at the end of all these words.

■ Fit the words from the suitcase into the maze.
Some letters are given to help you.

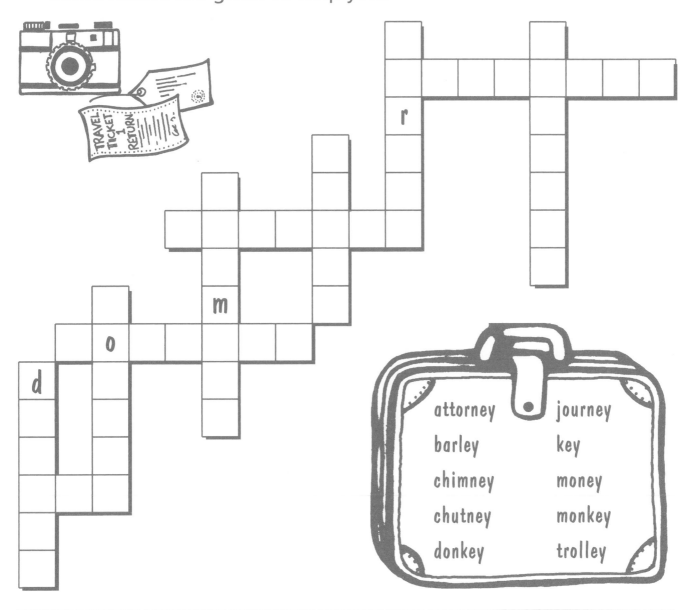

attorney   journey

barley   key

chimney   money

chutney   monkey

donkey   trolley

■ Use look, (say,) cover, write, check to practise each word.

_____   _____   _____   _____

_____   _____   _____

_____   _____

Tick here when you have checked your work.

Sheaves of **ves**

All the answers to this crossword are plurals of words which end in **f**.

■ Solve the clues and then explain the rule for all these rather odd plurals!

ACROSS

3. In autumn, these fall off the trees (6)
5. Baby cows (6)
7. Large animals, like big fierce dogs (6)
8. Small people like imps (5)
9. A book case has several of these (7)

DOWN

1. Two of these make a whole (6)
2. Bundles of corn or paper (7)
3. Large portions of bread (6)
4. We wear these to keep warm in winter (7)
6. A horse has four of these on the end of its feet (6)

■ Rule: To make these into plurals, change ____ to ____ and add ____.

■ Use look, (say,) cover, write, check to practise all the words.

_____ _____ _____ _____

_____ _____ _____

_____ _____

Tick here when you have checked your work. ☐

Stories of ies

To make a plural when a word ends in **y** after a consonant, we change the **y** to **i** and add **es**, e.g. story ⇨ stories; diary ⇨ diaries.

■ Write down the plural of each word, then find the <u>plurals</u> in the wordsearch.

1. baby ⇨ _____

2. cry ⇨ _____

3. curry ⇨ _____

4. entry ⇨ _____

5. forgery ⇨ _____

6. lady ⇨ _____

7. lorry ⇨ _____

8. mystery ⇨ _____

9. sky ⇨ _____

10. spy ⇨ _____

11. supply ⇨ _____

12. worry ⇨ _____

f	s	k	i	e	s	i
o	e	s	p	i	e	s
r	i	u	w	s	i	c
g	r	p	o	e	r	m
e	r	p	r	i	c	y
r	o	l	r	d	p	s
i	l	i	i	a	b	t
e	y	e	e	l	m	e
s	i	s	s	b	k	r
b	a	b	i	e	s	i
s	e	i	r	t	n	e
c	u	r	r	i	e	s

■ Use l**oo**k, (say,) cover, write, ch**e**ck ✔ to practise each <u>plural</u>.

_____ _____ _____

_____ _____ _____

_____ _____ _____

Tick here when you have checked your work. ☐

Pay attention to **tion**

Each row of bricks is hiding a word which ends in **tion**.

■ Colour in the bricks to find the words. The first one is done for you. Remember, don't colour in any of the extra bricks which are trying to trick you!

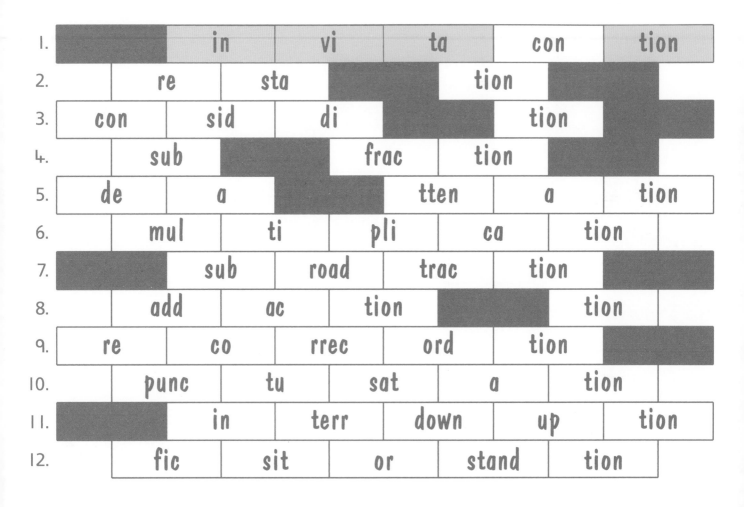

1.	in	vi	ta	con	tion
2.	re	sta		tion	
3.	con	sid	di		tion
4.	sub		frac	tion	
5.	de	a		tten	a	tion
6.	mul	ti	pli	ca	tion
7.		sub	road	trac	tion
8.	add	ac	tion		tion
9.	re	co	rrec	ord	tion
10.	punc	tu	sat	a	tion
11.		in	terr	down	up	tion
12.	fic	sit	or	stand	tion

■ Use look, say, cover, write, check to practise each word.

_____   _____   _____

_____   _____   _____

_____   _____   _____

_____   _____   _____

Tick here when you have checked your work. ☐

Page 26

Presenting **ent**

Words can be divided into smaller parts called syllables.
Each syllable has one beat,

e.g. **compliment** = **com** + **pli** + **ment** = 3 syllables.

■ Post these **ent** words into the correct post box.

absent	comment	fluent	parent
accident	confident	incident	present
argument	current	instrument	president

2 syllables

_____
_____
_____
_____
_____
_____

3 syllables

_____
_____
_____
_____
_____
_____

■ Use look, (say,) cover, write, check to practise all the words.

_____   _____   _____

_____   _____   _____

_____   _____   _____

Tick here when you have checked your work. ☐

Altering adjectives

Adjectives can change to show how one thing compares to another.

e.g. **small** ⇨ **sma**l**ler** ⇨ **sma**l**lest**

■ Use the endings **er** and **est** to fill in the missing words on each necklace.

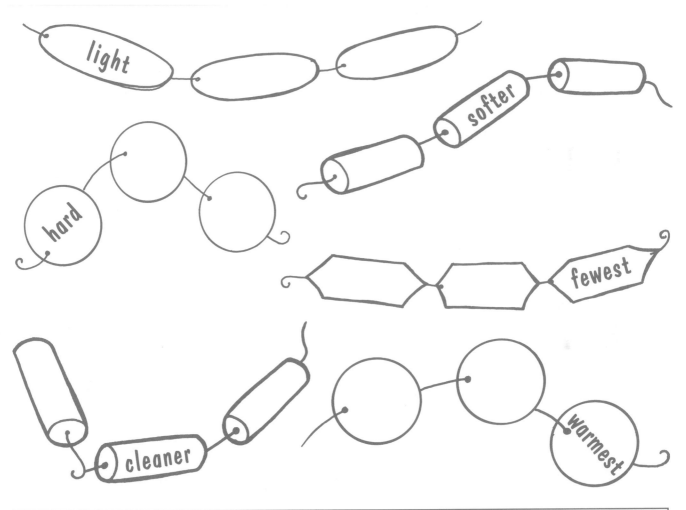

light

hard

softer

fewest

cleaner

warmest

■ Use **look**, **say**, **cover**, **write**, **check** to practise all the **er** and **est** words.

_____ _____ _____ _____

_____ _____ _____ _____

_____ _____ _____ _____

Tick here when you have checked your work. ☐

Altering adjectives 2

When we add **er** and **est** to an adjective which ends in a single consonant, we must remember to double the final consonant,

e.g. **big** ⇨ **bigger** ⇨ **biggest**

■ Fill in missing word on this wall of adjectives.

Don't forget to double consonants if you need to!

1.	hot	hotter	
2.	flat		
3.		higher	highest
4.	fast		fastest
5.		wettest	
6.		fatter	
7.	sharp		
8.			coldest
9.		darker	
10.	sadder		
11.	short		
12.	bright		

■ Use l⦿⦿k, (say,) cover, write, check ✓ to practise all the **er** and **est** words.

_____ _____ _____ _____ _____

_____ _____ _____ _____ _____

_____ _____ _____ _____ _____

_____ _____ _____ _____ _____

Tick here when you have checked your work. ☐

Varying verbs

Verbs change to tell us when something happened. They often use these endings when they change.

| s |
| ed   ing |

■ Can you put a different word for each verb's family on every rung of its ladder? One is done for you.

Remember – if there is only one consonant after the vowel (e.g. **ski̱p̱**, **ho̱p̱**) then the consonant is doubled when you add **ing** or **ed** (**ski̱p̱p̱ing**, **ho̱p̱p̱ed**).

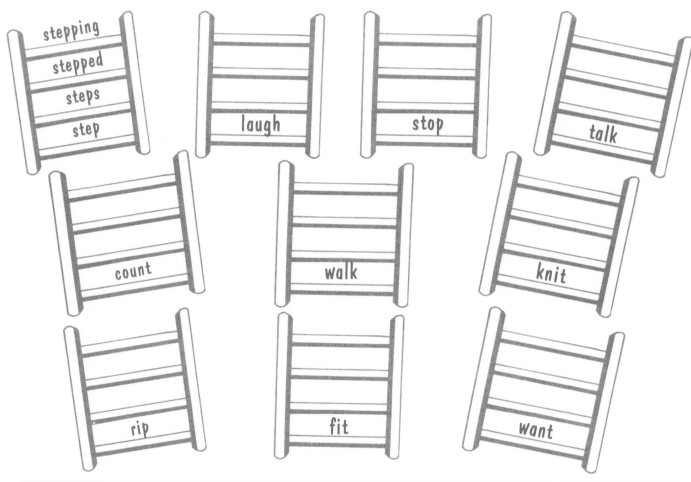

stepping
stepped
steps
step

laugh

stop

talk

count

walk

knit

rip

fit

want

■ Use l**oo**k, (**say,**) **cover**, write, ch**e**ck to practise all the **ing** and **ed** words.

_____ _____ _____ _____

_____ _____ _____ _____

_____ _____ _____ _____

_____ _____ _____

Tick here when you have checked your work. ☐

Megapuzzle

■ This puzzle contains at least one word from every puzzle in this book. Can you find them all?

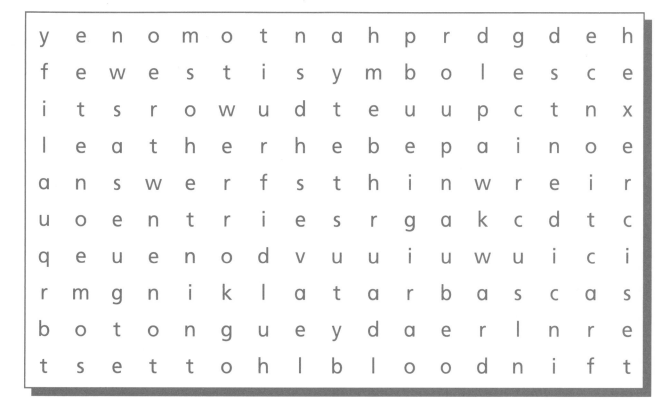

```
y  e  n  o  m  o  t  n  a  h  p  r  d  g  d  e  h
f  e  w  e  s  t  i  s  y  m  b  o  l  e  s  c  e
i  t  s  r  o  w  u  d  t  e  u  u  p  c  t  n  x
l  e  a  t  h  e  r  h  e  b  e  p  a  i  n  o  e
a  n  s  w  e  r  f  s  t  h  i  n  w  r  e  i  r
u  o  e  n  t  r  i  e  s  r  g  a  k  c  d  t  c
q  e  u  e  n  o  d  v  u  u  i  u  w  u  i  c  i
r  m  g  n  i  k  l  a  t  a  r  b  a  s  c  a  s
b  o  t  o  n  g  u  e  y  d  a  e  r  l  n  r  e
t  s  e  t  t  o  h  l  b  l  o  o  d  n  i  f  t
```

answer	fewest	leaves	symbol
awkward	fraction	money	talking
birth	fruit	numb	tongue
blood	glue	phantom	witch
circus	hottest	qualify	worst
done	incident	ready	yesterday
doubt	knee	ripped	
entries	laughed	someone	
exercise	leather	sure	

■ Arrange the ten unused letters to find the mystery word.

_ _ _ _ _ _ _ _ _ _

Congratulations, you have finished this workbook!

Schofield&Sims

the long-established educational publisher
specialising in maths, English and science materials for schools

New Spellaway is a series of graded activity books containing puzzles and activities designed to reinforce spelling using the widely recommended 'look, say, cover, write, check' method.

New Spellaway Book 2 includes:

- Silent letters in words (for example, 'w' in wriggle and 'k' in kneel)
- The 'qua' sound
- Compound words
- Word endings 'tch' and 'ey'
- Plurals ('ies' and 'ves').

This book is suitable for children in Key Stage 2.

The full range of titles in the series is as follows:

New Spellaway Book 1:   ISBN 978 07217 0847 8

New Spellaway Book 2:   ISBN 978 07217 0848 5

New Spellaway Book 3:   ISBN 978 07217 0849 2

New Spellaway Book 4:   ISBN 978 07217 0850 8

Springboard by Schofield & Sims?

...ity books reinforcing key aspects of literacy such as ...n, vocabulary and reading comprehension.

For further information and to place your order visit www.schofieldandsims.co.uk or telephone 01484 607080

ISBN 978-07217-0848-5

Schofield&Sims

Dogley Mill, Fenay Bridge, Huddersfield HD8 0NQ
Phone: 01484 607080 Facsimile: 01484 606815
E-mail: sales@schofieldandsims.co.uk
www.schofieldandsims.co.uk

ISBN 978 07217 0848 5

£2.95
(Retail price)

Key Stage 2
Age range: 7–11 years